This Book Belongs to:

Special thanks to:
My loving husband, Ryan. my precious children. our past and present churches.
my parents and in-loves. my sister. my grandparents, my Titus 2 women, X.G.,
missionary friends, our dearest friends and family,
the random parents from the park who allowed me to test read this book to their children.
And all of the Cinnamon Rolls.

Text and Illustrations Copyright © 2022 Rachel Benham
Illustrations created in paper and ink.
Typeset in Times Neue Roman, Scripter
ISBN: 978-1-7379387-1-2
Library of Congress Control Number: 2022917488

All rights reserved. No part of this book may be reproduced in any form without written permission from the publisher,
except by reviewers who may use a brief passage in a review.

Scripture quotations marked CSB have been taken from the Christian Standard Bible®, Copyright © 2017 by Holman Bible Publishers. Used by permission. Christian Standard Bible® and CSB® are federally registered trademarks of Holman Bible Publishers.

Scripture quotations Scripture quotations marked (ESV) are from The ESV® Bible (The Holy Bible, English Standard Version®), copyright © 2001 by Crossway, a publishing ministry of Good News Publishers. Used by permission. All rights reserved.

"Scripture quotations taken from the (NASB®) New American Standard Bible®, Copyright © 1995, by The Lockman Foundation. Used by permission. All rights reserved. www.lockman.org"

Please consider asking your Library to order a copy of this book.

Joyful Kids Publishing, LLC- Rapid City, SD 57702
inquiries@joyfulkidspublishing.com
@Joyfulkidspublishing
@RachelLBenham

For: Our Children and generations to come.
May this book point you to your Savior!

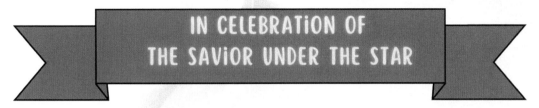

**IN CELEBRATION OF
THE SAVIOR UNDER THE STAR**

This adorable book is sure to become part of our regular reading time—especially around Christmas! Rachel tells the story of Jesus' birth and the hope we find there. I love the artwork the message of hope that fills each page. A perfect gift!
—Lisa Leonard Jewelry Designer + Author

As I read The Savior Under the Star, I imagined reading it on Christmas Eve as my family sat around a beautifully decorated tree. The illustrations are so well done and appropriate. The words are Biblical and age appropriate. It's the kind of book that becomes a family legacy. The Savior is glorified.
-Pastor Don Smith, Director of Barnabas Brothers Ministry, San Clemente, CA

Our customers have already raved about Rachel's previous work and I know they will be even more impressed by what she has done with "The Savior Under The Star." Her artwork is unique and the storyline's steady rhythm is easy to follow. We love this book because not only does it tell the story of the manger but everything Jesus did for us after and why we truly celebrate His birth.
-Brittany Sadler Founder of FaithLit LLC

May the Lord use this book
for His Glory!

Dear Reader,

You may have heard this story more than once— Shepherds, lambs, wise men, a baby born in a manger, busy inns, a bright star, and lovely animals that were present at the birth of Jesus. However, there's so much MORE to this story!

After sin entered the world, God promised He would send a Savior through a descendent of Adam and Eve, who would crush the head of Satan (Genesis 3:15). This was God's first promise of the coming of a Savior! People prayed, hoped, and prophesied about the birth of Jesus for a very long time (Isaiah 53). Sin was a major problem for everyone. The Bible tells us that all have sinned and fallen short of the Glory of God. (Romans 3:23)

Jesus entered the world being fully God and fully man. He lived a perfect life. He suffered the penalty of sin and death on our behalf. Jesus became the ultimate sacrifice. When we follow Christ, Jesus puts His righteousness on us. (1 Corinthians 1:30)

My hope is that your faith will grow while reading the pages of this book, that you will learn more about the rich heritage that we have in the full story of Jesus Christ.

I wrote this children's book, with the intention to create something that families could enjoy, discuss, and use to draw closer to our Savior. My prayer is that this book will encourage you in your walk with the Lord. The Bible passages that inspired me to write The Savior under the Star, are included in the back of this book. I've organized them into a 25-day reading plan that's perfect for the advent season or any time of year!

Love In Christ,

Rachel

There is a baby
under that

STAR!

How did he get there?
Did he come from afar?

His story starts a long time ago; before the sun cast a shadow, or the stars were aglow!

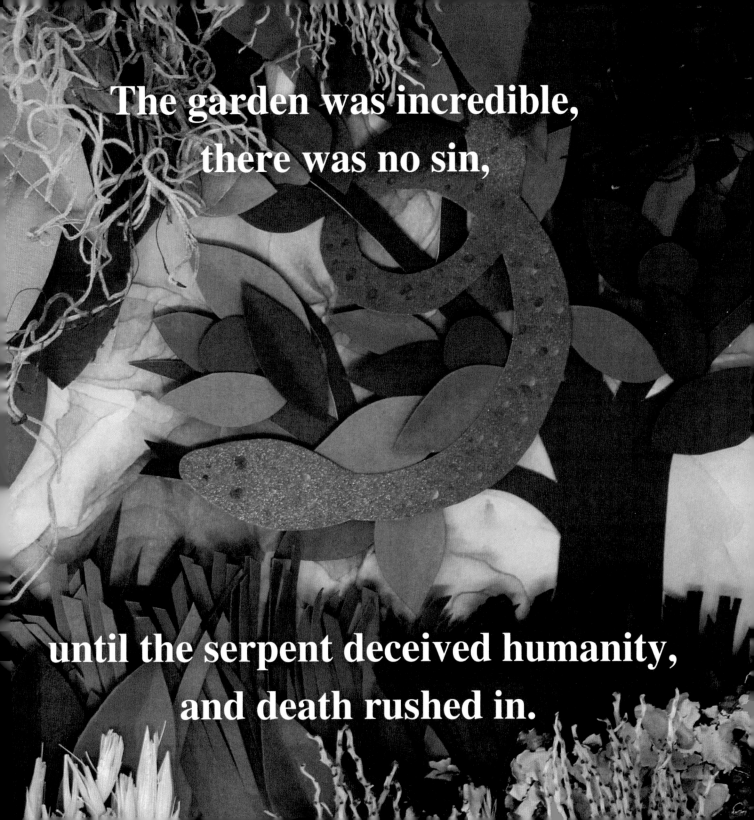

The garden was incredible,
there was no sin,

until the serpent deceived humanity,
and death rushed in.

The people were sad,
separated from
The Creator of all.

Humanity needed to be
rescued after the fall.

Gone were
the days of walking
next to the Lord.

Perfection was a
price they could
never afford.

Humanity waited and asked for a

They needed a savior above anything.

God had a plan
and revealed it to some.
He told the prophets

THE REDEEMER WOULD COME!

A young virgin named

Mary

would never be the same,
when an Angel came down
and called her by name!

Mary was told

"Do not be afraid."

God was keeping
all the promises

He had made!

Mary had
The Savior
growing in her
womb.
Someday,
He would
amazingly rise
from a tomb!

Mary rose up with
news to tell.
She told Elizabeth
of her baby,

Emmanuel!

Elizabeth had a
miracle leaping in
her womb!
Her baby, John,
jumped when Mary
entered the room.

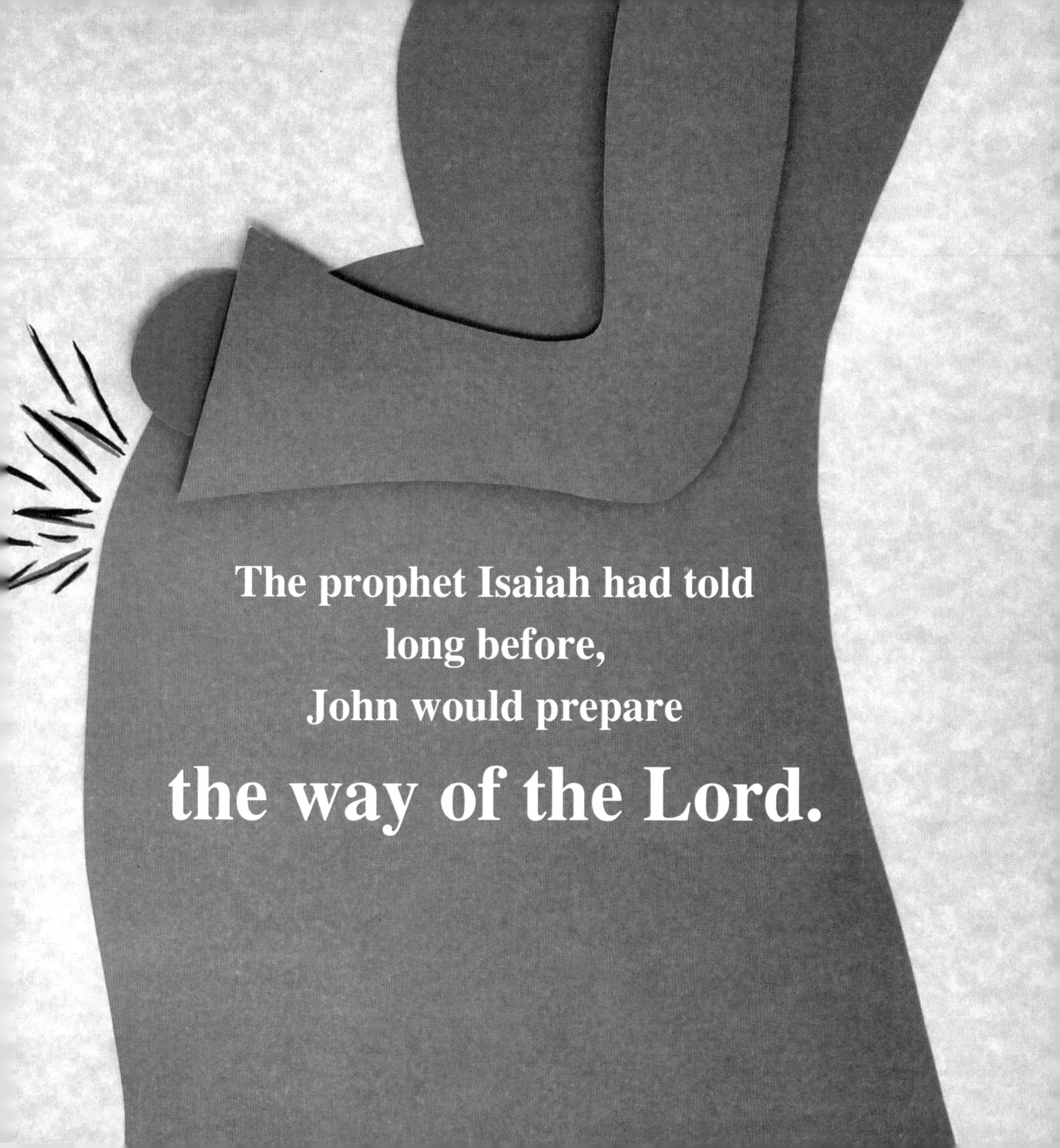

The prophet Isaiah had told
long before,
John would prepare
the way of the Lord.

When Mary came to Joseph, her husband to be,
she spoke of the baby.
He wanted to flee.

An Angel appeared to
Joseph in a dream.
He was told to
wed Mary.
It was not as it
seemed!

Joseph took Mary to be counted as his wife.
She walked the long dusty road to Bethlehem,
carrying this precious life.

Arriving in Bethlehem,
it was time for the baby to come!
The inns were full, there was
no room to be found
for God's only Son!

Finding a stable they snuggled in tight...

the baby boy would be born that night!

Shepherds nearby were taking care of their sheep.

When an ANGEL showed up they couldn't say a peep.

The shepherds hurried as fast as can be,
to find baby Jesus
sleeping peacefully.

That night a
STAR
rose over the Savior King!

The wise men rose up
with gifts to bring!

Knowing **THE STAR** was for the King of the Jews, they went to King Herod to find out the news.

"WHERE IS THIS KING?" They inquired of him. Herod couldn't answer. His heart was full of sin.

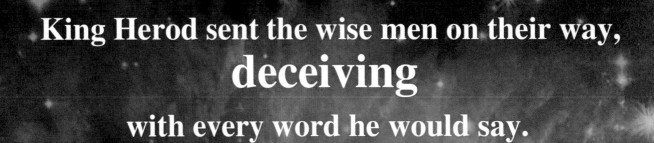

King Herod sent the wise men on their way,
deceiving
with every word he would say.

Asking the wise men to
return to him,
Herod planned to
destroy Jesus,
instead of
worshipping Him.

The wise men followed the

STAR

that was shining so bright,
traveling long distances deep
into the night.

Oh the joy they felt seeing Jesus under that
STAR!

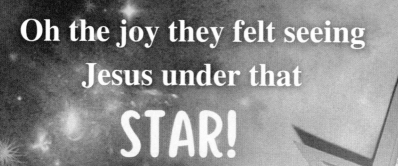

Bringing The Savior gold, frankincense, and myrrh from afar!

The wise men had a dream that Herod was bad. They didn't return and that made Herod very mad.

Joseph led his family to Egypt
after the Lord appeared in a dream,
fulfilling old prophecy.

They hid Jesus from Herod
who was being horribly mean.

That sweet Savior
who was under the
STAR...

He was much more
than a baby,
by far!

Jesus would live a

HOLY LIFE.

He would be the

PERFECT SACRIFICE,

the end to humanity's sinful strife.

Jesus would teach and pray,
and do miracles during
the day.

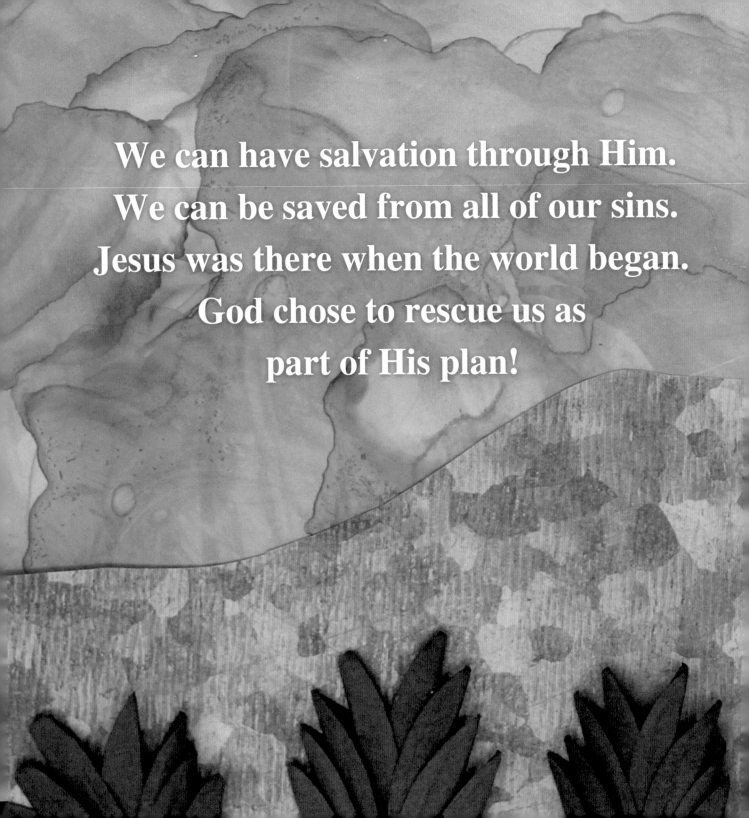

We can have salvation through Him.
We can be saved from all of our sins.
Jesus was there when the world began.
God chose to rescue us as
part of His plan!

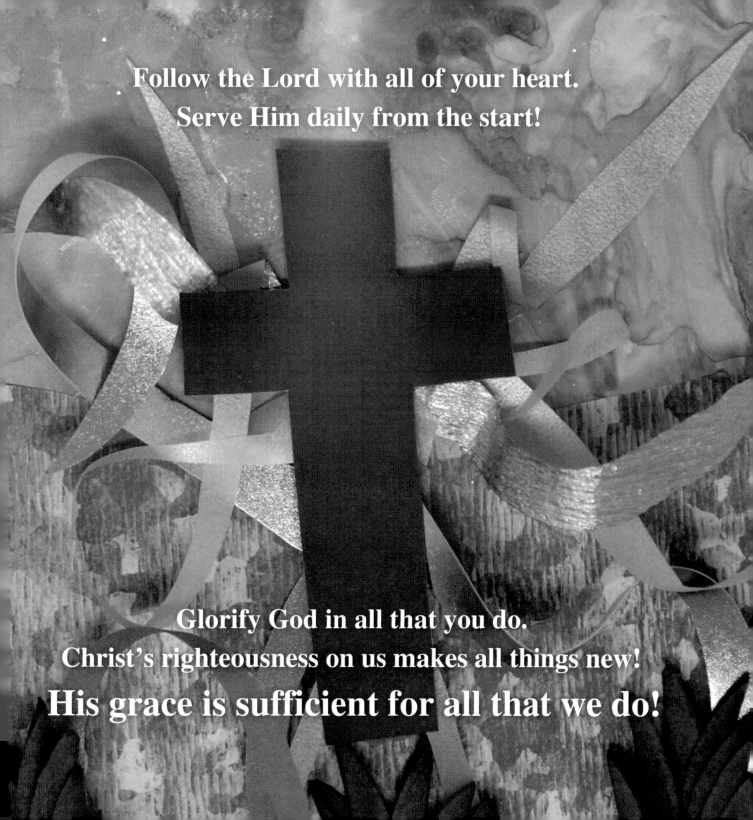

Follow the Lord with all of your heart.
Serve Him daily from the start!

Glorify God in all that you do.
Christ's righteousness on us makes all things new!
His grace is sufficient for all that we do!

Ask God to redeem you from your sins.
When we repent, our new life begins!

So...
Who is
that baby
under the
STAR?

That's our Savior,

KiNG JESUS!

He is much more
than a baby, by far!

Discussion Questions:

Why did humanity (people) need a Savior?

Because all people have sinned.

Romans 5:12 (ESV)

Therefore, just as sin came into the world through one man, and death through sin, and so death spread to all men because all sinned.

What does Savior mean?

Jesus is our Savior, He came to save, rescue, and deliver us from death.

1 Timothy 1:15-17 (ESV)

The saying is trustworthy and deserving of full acceptance, that Christ Jesus came into the world to save sinners, of whom I am the foremost. 16 But I received mercy for this reason, that in me, as the foremost, Jesus Christ might display his perfect patience as an example to those who were to believe in him for eternal life. 17 To the King of the ages, immortal, invisible, the only God, be honor and glory forever and ever. Amen.

How to do we follow God?

By loving Him, believing in Him, repenting of our sins, and loving our neighbors.

Romans 10:9 (ESV)

because, if you confess with your mouth that Jesus is Lord and believe in your heart that God raised him from the dead, you will be saved.

Matthew 22:37–40 (ESV)

And he said to him, "You shall love the Lord your God with all your heart and with all your soul and with all your mind. 38 This is the great and first commandment. 39 And a second is like it: You shall love your neighbor as yourself. 40 On these two commandments depend all the Law and the Prophets."

John 3:16–18 (ESV)

"For God so loved the world, that he gave his only Son, that whoever believes in him should not perish but have eternal life. 17 For God did not send his Son into the world to condemn the world, but in order that the world might be saved through him. 18 Whoever believes in him is not condemned, but whoever does not believe is condemned already, because he has not believed in the name of the only Son of God.

What is sin?

Sin is anything we say, think or do that disobeys God and goes against His commands.

Romans 5:18-19 (ESV)

Therefore, as one trespass led to condemnation for all men, so one act of righteousness leads to justification and life for all men. 19 For as by the one man's disobedience the many were made sinners, so by the one man's obedience the many will be made righteous.

1 John 1:8-9 (ESV)

If we say we have no sin, we deceive ourselves, and the truth is not in us. 9 If we confess our sins, he is faithful and just to forgive us our sins and to cleanse us from all unrighteousness.

How does Jesus rescue us from our sins?

He was the ultimate sacrifice, Jesus paid for our sins by dying on the cross for us. When we put our faith in His work on the cross and His resurrection, God graciously forgives us of our sins and He sees Jesus' righteousness on us. We have salvation by grace alone, through faith alone, in Christ alone.

Ephesians 2:1-10 (ESV)

And you were dead in the trespasses and sins 2 in which you once walked, following the course of this world, following the prince of the power of the air, the spirit that is now at work in the sons of disobedience— 3 among whom we all once lived in the passions of our flesh, carrying out the desires of the body and the mind, and were by nature children of wrath, like the rest of mankind. 4 But God, being rich in mercy, because of the great love with which he loved us, 5 even when we were dead in our trespasses, made us alive together with Christ—by grace you have been saved—6 and raised us up with him and seated us with him in the heavenly places in Christ Jesus, 7 so that in the coming ages he might show the immeasurable riches of his grace in kindness toward us in Christ Jesus. 8 For by grace you have been saved through faith. And this is not your own doing; it is the gift of God, 9 not a result of works, so that noone may boast. 10 For we are his workmanship, created in Christ Jesus for good works, which God prepared beforehand, that we should walk in them.

1 John 2:1-6 (ESV)

My little children, I am writing these things to you so that you may not sin. But if anyone does sin, we have an advocate with the Father, Jesus Christ the righteous. 2 He is the propitiation for our sins, and not for ours only but also for the sins of the whole world. 3 And by this we know that we have come to know him, if we keep his commandments. 4 Whoever says "I know him" but does not keep his commandments is a liar, and the truth is not in him, 5 but whoever keeps his word, in him truly the love of God is perfected. By this we may know that we are in him: 6 whoever says he abides in him ought to walk in the same way in which he walked.

Dear Reader,

Every night our family gathers for "Family Bible Time." We didn't always find it simple or routine to do this, honestly it was hard, but one Christmas season we followed a reading plan and it forever changed our family culture.

We read 1-2 chapters in the Bible followed by discussion, prayer, and worship. Whether or not you are already participating in a family devotional plan, I hope you will consider reading through these carefully chosen passages that this book was based upon. For the next 25 days, I encourage you to Feast on God's word together, the best truths are found in scripture.

Many blessings to you and your loved ones.

Hebrews 4:12 (ESV)
For the word of God is living and active, sharper than any two-edged sword, piercing to the division of soul and of spirit, of joints and of marrow, and discerning the thoughts and intentions of the heart.

Advent Readings

Day 1
Jesus and Creation

John 1:1-5 (ESV)

In the beginning was the Word, and the Word was with God, and the Word was God. He was in the beginning with God. All things were made through him, and without him was not any thing made that was made. In him was life, and the life was the light of men. The light shines in the darkness, and the darkness has not overcome it.

Hebrews 1:10-12 (ESV)

And, "You, Lord, laid the foundation of the earth in the beginning, and the heavens are the work of your hands; they will perish, but you remain; they will all wear out like a garment, like a robe you will roll them up, like a garment they will be changed. But you are the same, and your years will have no end."

Genesis 1:1-5 (ESV)

In the beginning, God created the heavens and the earth. The earth was without form and void, and darkness was over the face of the deep. And the Spirit of God was hovering over the face of the waters.
And God said, "Let there be light," and there was light. And God saw that the light was good. And God separated the light from the darkness. God called the light Day, and the darkness he called Night. And there was evening and there was morning, the first day.

Day 2
God Creates Man and Woman

Genesis 1:26-27 (NASB)

Then God said, "Let Us make man in Our image, according to Our likeness; and let them rule over the fish of the sea and over the birds of the sky and over the cattle and over all the earth, and over every creeping thing that creeps on the earth." God created man in His own image, in the image of God He created him; male and female He created them.

Genesis 2:5-9 (NASB)

Now no shrub of the field was yet in the earth, and no plant of the field had yet sprouted, for the Lord God had not sent rain upon the earth, and there was no man to cultivate the ground. But a mist used to rise from the earth and water the whole surface of the ground. Then the Lord God formed man of dust from the ground, and breathed into his nostrils the breath of life; and man became a living being. The Lord God planted a garden toward the east, in Eden; and there He placed the man whom He had formed. Out of the ground the Lord God caused to grow every tree that is pleasing to the sight and good for food; the tree of life also in the midst of the garden, and the tree of the knowledge of good and evil.

Genesis 2:15-25 (NASB)

Then the Lord God took the man and put him into the garden of Eden to cultivate it and keep it. The Lord God commanded the man, saying, "From any tree of the garden you may eat freely; but from the tree of the knowledge of good and evil you shall not eat, for in the day that you eat from it you will surely die."

Then the Lord God said, "It is not good for the man to be alone; I will make him a helper suitable for him." Out of the ground the Lord God formed every beast of the field and every bird of the sky, and brought them to the man to see what he would call them; and whatever the man called a living creature, that was its name. The man gave names to all the cattle, and to the birds of the sky, and to every beast of the field, but for Adam there was not found a helper suitable for him. So the Lord God caused a deep sleep to fall upon the man, and he slept; then He took one of his ribs and closed up the flesh at that place. The Lord God fashioned into a woman the rib which He had taken from the man, and brought her to the man. The man said,

"This is now bone of my bones, And flesh of my flesh; She shall be called Woman, Because she was taken out of Man."

For this reason a man shall leave his father and his mother, and be joined to his wife; and they shall become one flesh. And the man and his wife were both naked and were not ashamed.

Day 3
The Serpent Deceived and Sin Entered the Garden

Genesis 3:1-13 (CSB)

Now the serpent was the most cunning of all the wild animals that the Lord God had made. He said to the woman, "Did God really say, 'You can't eat from any tree in the garden'?" The woman said to the serpent, "We may eat the fruit from the trees in the garden. But about the fruit of the tree in the middle of the garden, God said, 'You must not eat it or touch it, or you will die.'"

"No! You will certainly not die," the serpent said to the woman. "In fact, God knows that when you eat it your eyes will be opened and you will be like God, knowing good and evil." The woman saw that the tree was good for food and delightful to look at, and that it was desirable for obtaining wisdom. So she took some of its fruit and ate it; she also gave some to her husband, who was with her, and he ate it. Then the eyes of both of them were opened, and they knew they were naked; so they sewed fig leaves together and made coverings for themselves.

Then the man and his wife heard the sound of the Lord God walking in the garden at the time of the evening breeze, and they hid from the Lord God among the trees of the garden. So the Lord God called out to the man and said to him, "Where are you?" And he said, "I heard you in the garden, and I was afraid because I was naked, so I hid." Then he asked, "Who told you that you were naked? Did you eat from the tree that I commanded you not to eat from?"

The man replied, "The woman you gave to be with me—she gave me some fruit from the tree, and I ate." So the Lord God asked the woman, "What have you done?" And the woman said, "The serpent deceived me, and I ate."

Day 4
They asked for a King, but Needed a Savior

1 Samuel 8:4-9 (CSB)

So all the elders of Israel gathered together and went to Samuel at Ramah. They said to him, "Look, you are old, and your sons do not walk in your ways. Therefore, appoint a king to judge us the same as all the other nations have."

When they said, "Give us a king to judge us," Samuel considered their demand wrong, so he prayed to the Lord. But the Lord told him, "Listen to the people and everything they say to you. They have not rejected you; they have rejected me as their king. They are doing the same thing to you that they have done to me, since the day I brought them out of Egypt until this day, abandoning me and worshiping other gods. Listen to them, but solemnly warn them and tell them about the customary rights of the king who will reign over them."

Job 34:10-15 (CSB)

Therefore listen to me, you men of understanding. It is impossible for God to do wrong, and for the Almighty to act unjustly. For he repays a person according to his deeds, and he gives him what his conduct deserves. Indeed, it is true that God does not act wickedly and the Almighty does not pervert justice. Who gave him authority over the earth? Who put him in charge of the entire world? If he put his mind to it and withdrew the spirit and breath he gave, every living thing would perish together and mankind would return to the dust.

Romans 5:12-14 (ESV)

Therefore, just as sin came into the world through one man, and death through sin, and so death spread to all men because all sinned— for sin indeed was in the world before the law was given, but sin is not counted where there is no law. Yet death reigned from Adam to Moses, even over those whose sinning was not like the transgression of Adam, who was a type of the one who was to come.

Day 5
Our Need for a Savior

Psalm 14:1-3 (CSB)

The fool says in his heart, "There's no God."

They are corrupt; they do vile deeds.

There is no one who does good.

The Lord looks down from heaven on the human race to see if there is one who is wise, one who seeks God. All have turned away; all alike have become corrupt. There is no one who does good,

not even one.

Romans 3:10-18 (ESV)

as it is written:

"None is righteous, no, not one;

no one understands; no one seeks for God.

All have turned aside; together they have become worthless; no one does good, not even one."

"Their throat is an open grave; they use their tongues to deceive."

"The venom of asps is under their lips."

"Their mouth is full of curses and bitterness."

"Their feet are swift to shed blood;

in their paths are ruin and misery,

and the way of peace they have not known."

"There is no fear of God before their eyes."

Ecclesiastes 7:20 (ESV)

Surely there is not a righteous man on earth who does good and never sins.

Genesis 6:5 (ESV)

The Lord saw that the wickedness of man was great in the earth, and that every intention of the thoughts of his heart was only evil continually.

Do not despair, dear friend. Here is a 'sneak peek'!
Good news is coming!

Acts 13:23 (ESV)

Of this man's offspring God has brought to Israel a Savior, Jesus, as he promised.

Luke 4:14-21 (CSB)

Then Jesus returned to Galilee in the power of the Spirit, and news about him spread throughout the entire vicinity. He was teaching in their synagogues, being praised by everyone. He came to Nazareth, where he had been brought up. As usual, he entered the synagogue on the Sabbath day and stood up to read. The scroll of the prophet Isaiah was given to him, and unrolling the scroll, he found the place where it was written: The Spirit of the Lord is on me, because he has anointed me to preach good news to the poor. He has sent me to proclaim release to the captives and recovery of sight to the blind, to set free the oppressed, to proclaim the year of the Lord's favor. He then rolled up the scroll, gave it back to the attendant, and sat down. And the eyes of everyone in the synagogue were fixed on him. He began by saying to them, "Today as you listen, this Scripture has been fulfilled."

Day 6
John the Baptist Fulfills Prophecy

Isaiah 40:3-5 (ESV)

A voice cries: "In the wilderness prepare the way of the Lord; make straight in the desert a highway for our God. Every valley shall be lifted up, and every mountain and hill be made low; the uneven ground shall become level, and the rough places a plain. And the glory of the Lord shall be revealed, and all flesh shall see it together for the mouth of the Lord has spoken."

Malachi 3:1 (ESV)

Behold, I send my messenger, and he will prepare the way before me. And the Lord whom you seek will suddenly come to his temple; and the messenger of the covenant in whom you delight, behold, he is coming, says the Lord of hosts.

Luke 1:5-25 (CSB)

In the days of King Herod of Judea, there was a priest of Abijah's divisionnamed Zechariah. His wife was from the daughters of Aaron, and her name was Elizabeth. Both were righteous in God's sight, living without blameaccording to all the commands and requirements of the Lord. But they had no children because Elizabeth could not conceive, and both of them were well along in years. When his division was on duty and he was serving as priest before God, it happened that he was chosen by lot, according to the custom of the priesthood, to enter the sanctuary of the Lord and burn incense. At the hour of incense the whole assembly of the people was praying outside. An angel of the Lord appeared to him, standing to the right of the altar of incense.

When Zechariah saw him, he was terrified and overcome with fear. But the angel said to him, "Do not be afraid, Zechariah, because your prayer has been heard. Your wife Elizabeth will bear you a son, and you will name him John. There will be joy and delight for you, and many will rejoice at his birth. For he will be great in the sight of the Lord and will never drink wine or beer. He will be filled with the Holy Spirit while still in his mother's womb. He will turn many of the children of Israel to the Lord their God. And he will go before him in the spirit and power of Elijah, to turn the hearts of fathers to their children, and the disobedient to the understanding of the righteous, to make ready for the Lord a prepared people."

"How can I know this?" Zechariah asked the angel. "For I am an old man, and my wife is well along in years."

The angel answered him, "I am Gabriel, who stands in the presence of God, and I was sent to speak to you and tell you this good news. Now listen. You will become silent and unable to speak until the day these things take place, because you did not believe my words, which will be fulfilled in their proper time."

Meanwhile, the people were waiting for Zechariah, amazed that he stayed so long in the sanctuary. When he did come out, he could not speak to them. Then they realized that he had seen a vision in the sanctuary. He was making signs to them and remained speechless. When the days of his ministry were completed, he went back home.

After these days his wife Elizabeth conceived and kept herself in seclusion for five months. She said, "The Lord has done this for me. He has looked with favor in these days to take away my disgrace among the people."

Day 7
The Angel Visits Mary

Luke 1:26-38 (NASB)

Now in the sixth month the angel Gabriel was sent from God to a city in Galilee called Nazareth, to a virgin engaged to a man whose name was Joseph, of the descendants of David; and the virgin's name was Mary. And coming in, he said to her, "Greetings, favored one! The Lord is with you." But she was very perplexed at this statement, and kept pondering what kind of salutation this was. The angel said to her, "Do not be afraid, Mary; for you have found favor with God. And behold, you will conceive in your womb and bear a son, and you shall name Him Jesus. He will be great and will be called the Son of the Most High; and the Lord God will give Him the throne of His father David; and He will reign over the house of Jacob forever, and His kingdom will have no end." Mary said to the angel, "How can this be, since I am a virgin?" The angel answered and said to her, "The Holy Spirit will come upon you, and the power of the Most High will overshadow you; and for that reason the holy Child shall be called the Son of God. And behold, even your relative Elizabeth has also conceived a son in her old age; and she who was called barren is now in her sixth month. For nothing will be impossible with God." And Mary said, "Behold, the bondslave of the Lord; may it be done to me according to your word." And the angel departed from her.

Day 8
Mary Visits Her Cousin, Elizabeth

Luke 1:39-56 (CSB)

In those days Mary set out and hurried to a town in the hill country of Judah where she entered Zechariah's house and greeted Elizabeth. When Elizabeth heard Mary's greeting, the baby leaped inside her, and Elizabeth was filled with the Holy Spirit. Then she exclaimed with a loud cry, "Blessed are you among women, and your child will be blessed! How could this happen to me, that the mother of my Lord should come to me? For you see, when the sound of your greeting reached my ears, the baby leaped for joy inside me. Blessed is she who has believed that the Lord would fulfill what he has spoken to her!"

And Mary said:

My soul magnifies the Lord, and my spirit rejoices in God my Savior, because he has looked with favor on the humble condition of his servant. Surely, from now on all generations will call me blessed, because the Mighty One has done great things for me, and his name is holy. His mercy is from generation to generation on those who fear him. He has done a mighty deed with his arm; he has scattered the proud because of the thoughts of their hearts; he has toppled the mighty from their thrones and exalted the lowly. He has satisfied the hungry with good things and sent the rich away empty. He has helped his servant Israel, remembering his mercy to Abraham and his descendants forever, just as he spoke to our ancestors. And Mary stayed with her about three months; then she returned to her home.

Day 9
John the Baptist is Born

Luke 1:57-80 (NASB)

Now the time had come for Elizabeth to give birth, and she gave birth to a son. Her neighbors and her relatives heard that the Lord had displayed His great mercy toward her; and they were rejoicing with her.

And it happened that on the eighth day they came to circumcise the child, and they were going to call him Zacharias, after his father. But his mother answered and said, "No indeed; but he shall be called John." And they said to her, "There is no one among your relatives who is called by that name." And they made signs to his father, as to what he wanted him called. And he asked for a tablet and wrote as follows, "His name is John." And they were all astonished. And at once his mouth was opened and his tongue loosed, and he began to speak in praise of God. Fear came on all those living around them; and all these matters were being talked about in all the hill country of Judea. All who heard them kept them in mind, saying,

"What then will this child turn out to be?" For the hand of the Lord was certainly with him.

And his father Zacharias was filled with the Holy Spirit, and prophesied, saying:

"Blessed be the Lord God of Israel,

For He has visited us and accomplished redemption for His people,

And has raised up a horn of salvation for us

In the house of David His servant—

As He spoke by the mouth of His holy prophets from of old—

Salvation from our enemies,

And from the hand of all who hate us;

To show mercy toward our fathers,

And to remember His holy covenant,

The oath which He swore to Abraham our father,

To grant us that we, being rescued from the hand of our enemies,

Might serve Him without fear,

In holiness and righteousness before Him all our days.

"And you, child, will be called the prophet of the Most High;

For you will go on before the Lord to prepare His ways;

To give to His people the knowledge of salvation

By the forgiveness of their sins,

Because of the tender mercy of our God,

With which the Sunrise from on high will visit us,

To shine upon those who sit in darkness and the shadow of death,

To guide our feet into the way of peace."

And the child continued to grow and to become strong in spirit, and he lived in the deserts until the day of his public appearance to Israel.

Day 10
Joseph Hears about Jesus

Matthew 1:18-25 (CSB)

The birth of Jesus Christ came about this way: After his mother Mary had been engaged to Joseph, it was discovered before they came together that she was pregnant from the Holy Spirit. So her husband, Joseph, being a righteous man, and not wanting to disgrace her publicly, decided to divorce her secretly.

But after he had considered these things, an angel of the Lord appeared to him in a dream, saying, "Joseph, son of David, don't be afraid to take Mary as your wife, because what has been conceived in her is from the Holy Spirit. She will give birth to a son, and you are to name him Jesus, because he will save his people from their sins."

Now all this took place to fulfill what was spoken by the Lord through the prophet:

See, the virgin will become pregnant
and give birth to a son,
and they will name him Immanuel,
which is translated "God is with us."

When Joseph woke up, he did as the Lord's angel had commanded him. He married her but did not have sexual relations with her until she gave birth to a son. And he named him Jesus.

Day 11
Mary and Joseph Travel to Bethlehem

Micah 5:2 (ESV)
But you, O Bethlehem Ephrathah,
who are too little to be among the clans of Judah,
from you shall come forth for me
one who is to be ruler in Israel,
whose coming forth is from of old,
from ancient days.

Luke 2:1-6 (ESV)
In those days a decree went out from Caesar Augustus that all the world should be registered. This was the first registration when Quirinius was governor of Syria. And all went to be registered, each to his own town. And Joseph also went up from Galilee, from the town of Nazareth, to Judea, to the city of David, which is called Bethlehem, because he was of the house and lineage of David, to be registered with Mary, his betrothed, who was with child.
And while they were there, the time came for her to give birth.

Day 12
Jesus is Born!

Zechariah 9:9 (ESV)
Rejoice greatly, O daughter of Zion!
 Shout aloud, O daughter of Jerusalem!
Behold, your king is coming to you;
 righteous and having salvation is he,
humble and mounted on a donkey,
 on a colt, the foal of a donkey.

Isaiah 7:14 (ESV)
Therefore the Lord himself will give you a sign. Behold, the virgin shall conceive and bear a son, and shall call his name Immanuel.

Luke 2:7 (ESV)
 And she gave birth to her firstborn son and wrapped him in swaddling cloths and laid him in a manger, because there was no place for them in the inn.

Matthew 1:23-25 (ESV)
 "Behold, the virgin shall conceive and bear a son,
 and they shall call his name Immanuel"
(which means, God with us). When Joseph woke from sleep, he did as the angel of the Lord commanded him: he took his wife, but knew her not until she had given birth to a son. And he called his name Jesus.

Day 13
The Shepherds and Angels

Luke 2:8-20 (NASB)

In the same region there were some shepherds staying out in the fields and keeping watch over their flock by night. And an angel of the Lord suddenly stood before them, and the glory of the Lord shone around them; and they were terribly frightened. But the angel said to them, "Do not be afraid; for behold, I bring you good news of great joy which will be for all the people; for today in the city of David there has been born for you a Savior, who is Christ the Lord. This will be a sign for you: you will find a baby wrapped in cloths and lying in a manger." And suddenly there appeared with the angel a multitude of the heavenly host praising God and saying,

 "Glory to God in the highest,
And on earth peace among men with whom He is pleased."

 When the angels had gone away from them into heaven, the shepherds began saying to one another, "Let us go straight to Bethlehem then, and see this thing that has happened which the Lord has made known to us." So they came in a hurry and found their way to Mary and Joseph, and the baby as He lay in the manger. When they had seen this, they made known the statement which had been told them about this Child. And all who heard it wondered at the things which were told them by the shepherds. But Mary treasured all these things, pondering them in her heart. The shepherds went back, glorifying and praising God for all that they had heard and seen, just as had been told them.

Day 14
Jesus was Presented at the Temple

Luke 2:21-40 (CSB)

When the eight days were completed for his circumcision, he was named Jesus—the name given by the angel before he was conceived. And when the days of their purification according to the law of Moses were finished, they brought him up to Jerusalem to present him to the Lord (just as it is written in the law of the Lord, Every firstborn male will be dedicated to the Lord) and to offer a sacrifice (according to what is stated in the law of the Lord, a pair of turtledoves or two young pigeons).

There was a man in Jerusalem whose name was Simeon. This man was righteous and devout, looking forward to Israel's consolation, and the Holy Spirit was on him. It had been revealed to him by the Holy Spirit that he would not see death before he saw the Lord's Messiah. Guided by the Spirit, he entered the temple. When the parents brought in the child Jesus to perform for him what was customary under the law, Simeon took him up in his arms, praised God, and said,

Now, Master, you can dismiss your servant in peace,
as you promised.
For my eyes have seen your salvation. You have prepared it
in the presence of all peoples—
a light for revelation to the Gentiles
and glory to your people Israel. His father and mother were amazed at what was being said about him. Then Simeon blessed them and told his mother Mary, "Indeed, this child is destined to cause the fall and rise of many in Israel and to be a sign that will be opposed— and a sword will pierce your own soul—that the thoughts of many hearts may be revealed."

There was also a prophetess, Anna, a daughter of Phanuel, of the tribe of Asher. She was well along in years, having lived with her husband seven years after her marriage, and was a widow for eighty-four years. She did not leave the temple, serving God night and day with fasting and prayers. At that very moment, she came up and began to thank God and to speak about him to all who were looking forward to the redemption of Jerusalem.

When they had completed everything according to the law of the Lord, they returned to Galilee, to their own town of Nazareth. The boy grew up and became strong, filled with wisdom, and God's grace was on him.

Day 15
The Wise men Follow the Star

Matthew 2:1-12 (CSB)

After Jesus was born in Bethlehem of Judea in the days of King Herod, wise men from the east arrived in Jerusalem, saying, "Where is he who has been born king of the Jews? For we saw his star at its rising and have come to worship him."

When King Herod heard this, he was deeply disturbed, and all Jerusalem with him. So he assembled all the chief priests and scribes of the people and asked them where the Messiah would be born. "In Bethlehem of Judea," they told him, "because this is what was written by the prophet: And you, Bethlehem, in the land of Judah, are by no means least among the rulers of Judah: Because out of you will come a ruler who will shepherd my people Israel."

Then Herod secretly summoned the wise men and asked them the exact time the star appeared. He sent them to Bethlehem and said, "Go and search carefully for the child. When you find him, report back to me so that I too can go and worship him."

After hearing the king, they went on their way. And there it was—the star they had seen at its rising. It led them until it came and stopped above the place where the child was. When they saw the star, they were overwhelmed with joy. Entering the house, they saw the child with Mary his mother, and falling to their knees, they worshiped him. Then they opened their treasures and presented him with gifts: gold, frankincense, and myrrh. And being warned in a dream not to go back to Herod, they returned to their own country by another route.

Day 16
Out of Egypt

Hosea 11:1 (ESV)

When Israel was a child, I loved him, and out of Egypt I called my son.

Matthew 2:13-23 (CSB)

After they were gone, an angel of the Lord appeared to Joseph in a dream, saying, "Get up! Take the child and his mother, flee to Egypt, and stay there until I tell you. For Herod is about to search for the child to kill him." So he got up, took the child and his mother during the night, and escaped to Egypt. He stayed there until Herod's death, so that what was spoken by the Lord through the prophet might be fulfilled: Out of Egypt I called my Son.

Then Herod, when he realized that he had been outwitted by the wise men, flew into a rage. He gave orders to massacre all the boys in and around Bethlehem who were two years old and under, in keeping with the time he had learned from the wise men. Then what was spoken through Jeremiah the prophet was fulfilled:

A voice was heard in Ramah, weeping, and great mourning,

Rachel weeping for her children; and she refused to be consoled, because they are no more. After Herod died, an angel of the Lord appeared in a dream to Joseph in Egypt, saying, "Get up, take the child and his mother, and go to the land of Israel, because those who intended to kill the child are dead." So he got up, took the child and his mother, and entered the land of Israel. But when he heard that Archelaus was ruling over Judea in place of his father Herod, he was afraid to go there. And being warned in a dream, he withdrew to the region of Galilee. Then he went and settled in a town called Nazareth to fulfill what was spoken through the prophets, that he would be called a Nazarene.

Day 17
Jesus as a Young Child

Luke 2:41-52 (NASB)

Now His parents went to Jerusalem every year at the Feast of the Passover. And when He became twelve, they went up there according to the custom of the Feast; and as they were returning, after spending the full number of days, the boy Jesus stayed behind in Jerusalem. But His parents were unaware of it, but supposed Him to be in the caravan, and went a day's journey; and they began looking for Him among their relatives and acquaintances. When they did not find Him, they returned to Jerusalem looking for Him. Then, after three days they found Him in the temple, sitting in the midst of the teachers, both listening to them and asking them questions. And all who heard Him were amazed at His understanding and His answers. When they saw Him, they were astonished; and His mother said to Him, "Son, why have You treated us this way? Behold, Your father and I have been anxiously looking for You." And He said to them, "Why is it that you were looking for Me? Did you not know that I had to be in My Father's house?" But they did not understand the statement which He had made to them. And He went down with them and came to Nazareth, and He continued in subjection to them; and His mother treasured all these things in her heart.

And Jesus kept increasing in wisdom and stature, and in favor with God and men.

Day 18
Jesus was Baptized by John

Luke 3:15-16 (ESV)

As the people were in expectation, and all were questioning in their hearts concerning John, whether he might be the Christ, John answered them all, saying, "I baptize you with water, but he who is mightier than I is coming, the strap of whose sandals I am not worthy to untie. He will baptize you with the Holy Spirit and fire.

Matthew 3:13-17 (ESV)

Then Jesus came from Galilee to the Jordan to John, to be baptized by him. John would have prevented him, saying, "I need to be baptized by you, and do you come to me?" But Jesus answered him, "Let it be so now, for thus it is fitting for us to fulfill all righteousness." Then he consented. And when Jesus was baptized, immediately he went up from the water, and behold, the heavens were opened to him, and he saw the Spirit of God descending like a dove and coming to rest on him; and behold, a voice from heaven said, "This is my beloved Son, with whom I am well pleased."

Acts 10: 36-38 (ESV)

As for the word that he sent to Israel, preaching good news of peace through Jesus Christ (he is Lord of all), you yourselves know what happened throughout all Judea, beginning from Galilee after the baptism that John proclaimed: how God anointed Jesus of Nazareth with the Holy Spirit and with power. He went about doing good and healing all who were oppressed by the devil, for God was with him.

Day 19
Jesus taught, Prayed, and Performed Miracles

Matthew 14:13-33 (CSB)

When Jesus heard about it, he withdrew from there by boat to a remote place to be alone. When the crowds heard this, they followed him on foot from the towns. When he went ashore, he saw a large crowd, had compassion on them, and healed their sick.

When evening came, the disciples approached him and said, "This place is deserted, and it is already late. Send the crowds away so that they can go into the villages and buy food for themselves."

"They don't need to go away," Jesus told them. "You give them something to eat."

"But we only have five loaves and two fish here," they said to him.

"Bring them here to me," he said. Then he commanded the crowds to sit down on the grass. He took the five loaves and the two fish, and looking up to heaven, he blessed them. He broke the loaves and gave them to the disciples, and the disciples gave them to the crowds. Everyone ate and was satisfied. They picked up twelve baskets full of leftover pieces. Now those who ate were about five thousand men, besides women and children.

Immediately he made the disciples get into the boat and go ahead of him to the other side, while he dismissed the crowds. After dismissing the crowds, he went up on the mountain by himself to pray. Well into the night, he was there alone. Meanwhile, the boat was already some distance from land, battered by the waves, because the wind was against them. Jesus came toward them walking on the sea very early in the morning. When the disciples saw him walking on the sea, they were terrified. "It's a ghost!" they said, and they cried out in fear.

Immediately Jesus spoke to them. "Have courage! It is I. Don't be afraid."

"Lord, if it's you," Peter answered him, "command me to come to you on the water."

He said, "Come."

And climbing out of the boat, Peter started walking on the water and came toward Jesus. But when he saw the strength of the wind, he was afraid, and beginning to sink he cried out, "Lord, save me!"

Immediately Jesus reached out his hand, caught hold of him, and said to him, "You of little faith, why did you doubt?"

When they got into the boat, the wind ceased. Then those in the boat worshiped him and said, "Truly you are the Son of God."

Day 20
Jesus Tells of His Death

Luke 9:18-36 (NASB)

And it happened that while He was praying alone, the disciples were with Him, and He questioned them, saying, "Who do the people say that I am?" They answered and said, "John the Baptist, and others say Elijah; but others, that one of the prophets of old has risen again." And He said to them, "But who do you say that I am?" And Peter answered and said, "The Christ of God." But He warned them and instructed them not to tell this to anyone, saying, "The Son of Man must suffer many things and be rejected by the elders and chief priests and scribes, and be killed and be raised up on the third day."

And He was saying to them all, "If anyone wishes to come after Me, he must deny himself, and take up his cross daily and follow Me. For whoever wishes to save his life will lose it, but whoever loses his life for My sake, he is the one who will save it. For what is a man profited if he gains the whole world, and loses or forfeits himself? For whoever is ashamed of Me and My words, the Son of Man will be ashamed of him when He comes in His glory, and the glory of the Father and of the holy angels. But I say to you truthfully, there are some of those standing here who will not taste death until they see the kingdom of God."

Some eight days after these sayings, He took along Peter and John and James, and went up on the mountain to pray. And while He was praying, the appearance of His face became different, and His clothing became white and gleaming. And behold, two men were talking with Him; and they were Moses and Elijah, who, appearing in glory, were speaking of His departure which He was about to accomplish at Jerusalem. Now Peter and his companions had been overcome with sleep; but when they were fully awake, they saw His glory and the two men standing with Him. And as these were leaving Him, Peter said to Jesus, "Master, it is good for us to be here; let us make three tabernacles: one for You, and one for Moses, and one for Elijah"—not realizing what he was saying. While he was saying this, a cloud formed and began to overshadow them; and they were afraid as they entered the cloud. Then a voice came out of the cloud, saying, "This is My Son, My Chosen One; listen to Him!" And when the voice had spoken, Jesus was found alone. And they kept silent, and reported to no one in those days any of the things which they had seen.

Day 21
Jesus was Crucified, He is our Savior

Isaiah 53:2-4 (ESV)

For he grew up before him like a young plant, and like a root out of dry ground; he had no form or majesty that we should look at him, and no beauty that we should desire him. He was despised and rejected by men, a man of sorrows and acquainted with grief; and as one from whom men hide their faces he was despised, and we esteemed him not. Surely he has borne our griefs and carried our sorrows; yet we esteemed him stricken, smitten by God, and afflicted.

John 19:1-6 (ESV)

Then Pilate took Jesus and flogged him. And the soldiers twisted together a crown of thorns and put it on his head and arrayed him in a purple robe. They came up to him, saying, "Hail, King of the Jews!" and struck him with their hands. Pilate went out again and said to them, "See, I am bringing him out to you that you may know that I find no guilt in him." So Jesus came out, wearing the crown of thorns and the purple robe. Pilate said to them, "Behold the man!" When the chief priests and the officers saw him, they cried out, "Crucify him, crucify him!" Pilate said to them, "Take him yourselves and crucify him, for I find no guilt in him."

Isaiah 53:5-6 (ESV)

But he was pierced for our transgressions; he was crushed for our iniquities; upon him was the chastisement that brought us peace, and with his wounds we are healed. All we like sheep have gone astray; we have turned—every one—to his own way; and the Lord has laid on him the iniquity of us all.

John 19:16-24 (ESV)

So he delivered him over to them to be crucified. So they took Jesus, and he went out, bearing his own cross, to the place called The Place of a Skull, which in Aramaic is called Golgotha. There they crucified him, and with him two others, one on either side, and Jesus between them. Pilate also wrote an inscription and put it on the cross. It read, "Jesus of Nazareth, the King of the Jews." Many of the Jews read this inscription, for the place where Jesus was crucified was near the city, and it was written in Aramaic, in Latin, and in Greek. So the chief priests of the Jews said to Pilate, "Do not write, 'The King of the Jews,' but rather, 'This man said, I am King of the Jews.'" Pilate answered, "What I have written I have written." When the soldiers had crucified Jesus, they took his garments and divided them into four parts, one part for each soldier; also his tunic. But the tunic was seamless, woven in one piece from top to bottom, so they said to one another, "Let us not tear it, but cast lots for it to see whose it shall be." This was to fulfill the Scripture which says,
"They divided my garments among them, and for my clothing they cast lots."

Psalm 22:16-18 (ESV)

For dogs encompass me; a company of evildoers encircles me; they have pierced my hands and feet I can count all my bones— they stare and gloat over me; they divide my garments among them, and for my clothing they cast lots.

Matthew 27:45-51 (ESV)

Now from the sixth hour there was darkness over all the land until the ninth hour. And about the ninth hour Jesus cried out with a loud voice, saying, "Eli, Eli, lema sabachthani?" that is, "My God, my God, why have you forsaken me?" And some of the bystanders, hearing it, said, "This man is calling Elijah." And one of them at once ran and took a sponge, filled it with sour wine, and put it on a reed and gave it to him to drink. But the others said, "Wait, let us see whether Elijah will come to save him." And Jesus cried out again with a loud voice and yielded up his spirit. And behold, the curtain of the temple was torn in two, from top to bottom. And the earth shook, and the rocks were split.

Day 22
Jesus Rose from the Dead, We are Reconciled

Matthew 28: 1-10 (NASB)

Now after the Sabbath, as it began to dawn toward the first day of the week, Mary Magdalene and the other Mary came to look at the grave. And behold, a severe earthquake had occurred, for an angel of the Lord descended from heaven and came and rolled away the stone and sat upon it. And his appearance was like lightning, and his clothing as white as snow. The guards shook for fear of him and became like dead men. The angel said to the women, "Do not be afraid; for I know that you are looking for Jesus who has been crucified. He is not here, for He has risen, just as He said. Come, see the place where He was lying. Go quickly and tell His disciples that He has risen from the dead; and behold, He is going ahead of you into Galilee, there you will see Him; behold, I have told you."

And they left the tomb quickly with fear and great joy and ran to report it to His disciples. And behold, Jesus met them and greeted them. And they came up and took hold of His feet and worshiped Him. Then Jesus said to them, "Do not be afraid; go and take word to My brethren to leave for Galilee, and there they will see Me."

Mark 16:2-8 (CSB)

Very early in the morning, on the first day of the week, they went to the tomb at sunrise. They were saying to one another, "Who will roll away the stone from the entrance to the tomb for us?" Looking up, they noticed that the stone—which was very large—had been rolled away.

When they entered the tomb, they saw a young man dressed in a whiterobe sitting on the right side; they were alarmed. "Don't be alarmed," he told them. "You are looking for Jesus of Nazareth, who was crucified. He has risen! He is not here. See the place where they put him. But go, tell his disciples and Peter, 'He is going ahead of you to Galilee; you will see him there just as he told you.'"

They went out and ran from the tomb, because trembling and astonishment overwhelmed them. And they said nothing to anyone, since they were afraid.

Romans 5:6-11 (ESV)

For while we were still weak, at the right time Christ died for the ungodly. For one will scarcely die for a righteous person—though perhaps for a good person one would dare even to die— but God shows his love for us in that while we were still sinners, Christ died for us. Since, therefore, we have now been justified by his blood, much more shall we be saved by him from the wrath of God. For if while we were enemies we were reconciled to God by the death of his Son, much more, now that we are reconciled, shall we be saved by his life. More than that, we also rejoice in God through our Lord Jesus Christ, through whom we have now received reconciliation.

Day 23
Jesus is our Savior!

John 14:1-7 (ESV)

"Let not your hearts be troubled. Believe in God; believe also in me. In my Father's house are many rooms. If it were not so, would I have told you that I go to prepare a place for you? And if I go and prepare a place for you, I will come again and will take you to myself, that where I am you may be also. And you know the way to where I am going." Thomas said to him, "Lord, we do not know where you are going. How can we know the way?" Jesus said to him, "I am the way, and the truth, and the life. No one comes to the Father except through me. If you had known me, you would have known my Father also. From now on you do know him and have seen him."

Hebrews 4:14-16 (ESV)

Since then we have a great high priest who has passed through the heavens, Jesus, the Son of God, let us hold fast our confession. For we do not have a high priest who is unable to sympathize with our weaknesses, but one who in every respect has been tempted as we are, yet without sin. Let us then with confidence draw near to the throne of grace, that we may receive mercy and find grace to help in time of need.

2 Corinthians 5:16-21 (NASB)

From now on, then, we do not know anyone from a worldly perspective. Even if we have known Christ from a worldly perspective, yet now we no longer know him in this way. Therefore, if anyone is in Christ, he is a new creation; the old has passed away, and see, the new has come! Everything is from God, who has reconciled us to himself through Christ and has given us the ministry of reconciliation. That is, in Christ, God was reconciling the world to himself, not counting their trespasses against them, and he has committed the message of reconciliation to us. Therefore, we are ambassadors for Christ, since God is making his appeal through us. We plead on Christ's behalf, "Be reconciled to God." He made the one who did not know sin to be sin for us, so that in him we might become the righteousness of God.

John 3:16-21 (NASB)

For God loved the world in this way: He gave his one and only Son, so that everyone who believes in him will not perish but have eternal life. For God did not send his Son into the world to condemn the world, but to save the world through him. Anyone who believes in him is not condemned, but anyone who does not believe is already condemned, because he has not believed in the name of the one and only Son of God. This is the judgment: The light has come into the world, and people loved darkness rather than the light because their deeds were evil. For everyone who does evil hates the light and avoids it, so that his deeds may not be exposed. But anyone who lives by the truth comes to the light, so that his works may be shown to be accomplished by God."

Day 24
Follow Jesus, Rejoice in Him!

Acts 1:6-11(ESV)

So when they had come together, they asked him, "Lord, will you at this time restore the kingdom to Israel?" He said to them, "It is not for you to know times or seasons that the Father has fixed by his own authority. But you will receive power when the Holy Spirit has come upon you, and you will be my witnesses in Jerusalem and in all Judea and Samaria, and to the end of the earth." And when he had said these things, as they were looking on, he was lifted up, and a cloud took him out of their sight. And while they were gazing into heaven as he went, behold, two men stood by them in white robes, and said, "Men of Galilee, why do you stand looking into heaven? This Jesus, who was taken up from you into heaven, will come in the same way as you saw him go into heaven."

Matthew 28:18-20 (ESV)

And Jesus came and said to them, "All authority in heaven and on earth has been given to me. Go therefore and make disciples of all nations, baptizing them in the name of the Father and of the Son and of the Holy Spirit, teaching them to observe all that I have commanded you. And behold, I am with you always, to the end of the age."

Romans 5:1-2 (ESV)

Therefore, since we have been justified by faith, we have peace with God through our Lord Jesus Christ. Through him we have also obtained access by faith into this grace in which we stand, and we rejoice in hope of the glory of God.

Day 25
Our Savior is on the Throne

Isaiah 9:6-7 (NASB)
For a child will be born to us, a son will be given to us;
And the government will rest on His shoulders;
And His name will be called Wonderful Counselor, Mighty God,
Eternal Father, Prince of Peace.
There will be no end to the increase of His government or of peace,
On the throne of David and over his kingdom,
To establish it and to uphold it with justice and righteousness
From then on and forevermore.
The zeal of the Lord of hosts will accomplish this.

Companion Coloring book available:

COMPANION COLORING BOOK
WITH BIBLE VERSES

The
Savior
Under
the Star

COLORING BOOK

Explore some additional books!

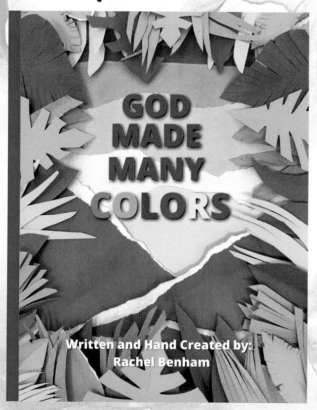

GOD MADE MANY COLORS

Written and Hand Created by:
Rachel Benham

You are Fearfully and Wonderfully Made!

Written and Hand Created by:
Rachel Benham

About the author:

Rachel is the author and illustrator of
The Savior Under the Star
You are Fearfully and Wonderfully Made!
and God Made Many Colors

Her joy and passion for The Gospel overflows into the children's books she writes and illustrates. The inventive art she creates for her books entices the eyes of little ones and adults alike!

Rachel can often be found homeschooling, discovering fun recipes in the kitchen, or sitting in the sunshine.

She loves spending time with her husband, Ryan and her two sons. They enjoy camping, fishing and learning everywhere they go.

Join her on Instagram at:
📷 @RachelLBenham

Made in the USA
Las Vegas, NV
20 November 2023

81215152R00052